WALT DISNEY PRODUCTIONS presents

Ali Baba
and the 40 Thieves

Random House  New York

Book Club Edition

Once there lived
a poor woodcutter
named Ali Baba.
Every day he went up
the hillside to chop wood.

His donkeys carried the wood to town where
Ali Baba sold it.

One day Ali Baba was loading wood onto his donkeys when he heard horses galloping down the path.

Ali Baba was scared.
It could be a gang of thieves.

Ali Baba quickly hid his
donkeys in the bushes.

Then he hid himself in
a tree.

The horsemen stopped in front of some large
rocks near Ali Baba's tree.

Then the leader cried out, "Open sesame!"

Suddenly one of the rocks swung open
like a door.

It was the entrance to a cave!

Ali Baba counted the horsemen as they rode inside.

Forty horsemen rode after the leader.

Finally the horsemen came out of
the cave and rode away.
The door swung shut behind them.

Ali Baba climbed down from
his tree and went to the door
of the cave.

Then he tried the
magic words.
"Open sesame!" he
cried.
The door
swung open.

The cave was
full of treasure
stolen by the thieves!

There were rolls
of fine silk, jars of
jewels, and sacks
of gold.

Ali Baba was very poor.
Since he knew the treasure belonged to
thieves, he decided to take some home.

He dragged a sackful of treasure out
of the cave, and the door swung shut.

The sack was very heavy.
He had to pull it to the place where
the donkeys were hidden.

When he reached the donkeys, he put the
treasure into the saddlebags on their backs.
Then he covered the bags with firewood
and started home.

It was late at night when Ali Baba got home.
"Where have you been?" asked his housekeeper.

"Shhh!" said Ali Baba. "Hurry with me to the courtyard so we can unload the donkeys."

When the housekeeper saw the gold and jewels, she was amazed.

"We have to hide this treasure," she said, "or someone will steal it."

"You are right," said Ali Baba.
They dug a hole in the floor and carefully buried the treasure.

The next day the thieves rode back to the cave.

Again the leader cried out, "Open sesame!"

Again the door of the cave swung open.

Inside they found broken jars and strange footprints.

"Someone has robbed us!" cried the leader. "Come. We must find him."

They followed the footprints to the place
where Ali Baba had cut his wood.

"The person who robbed us was a woodcutter,"
said the leader. "There is his ax."

When he got back to town, the leader looked everywhere for a woodcutter.

But he did not find Ali Baba.

Each time Ali Baba and his housekeeper wanted some of the treasure, they had to dig up the floor.

"What we need," said Ali Baba, "is a chest with a false bottom. Then we could reach the treasure easily."

"I'll go speak to a carpenter," said the housekeeper.

That night she went to a carpenter's house
and told him what they needed and that
it was a secret.

The carpenter said he could do the job.

The housekeeper blindfolded him so he would
not know where he was going.

Then she led him to
Ali Baba's house.

The carpenter worked quickly.
Before the night was over, he had made
a handsome chest with a false bottom.

Ali Baba and his housekeeper were very pleased.
After they paid the carpenter, the housekeeper
blindfolded him again and led him back to his house.

One day the leader of the gang of thieves happened to visit the carpenter.

"You work fast," said the leader.

"A few nights ago I worked even faster," said the carpenter. "In a few hours I built a chest with a false bottom to hide a secret treasure."

"If you take me to the place where you built that chest," said the leader, "I will pay you well."

"I was blindfolded when I went there, but if you also blindfold me, maybe I can find the house again."

That night the leader of the thieves
blindfolded the carpenter and
the carpenter retraced his steps to
Ali Baba's house.

The leader paid the carpenter and marked
the door of the house with an X.
The mark would help him to find the
house again.

The next morning the housekeeper found the X
on the door.

She was afraid the mark meant danger, so she
drew an X on every door along the street.

When the thieves came to find Ali Baba's house,
they did not know which one was his.

The leader was very angry.

That night the leader of the thieves again paid the carpenter to lead him to Ali Baba's house.

But this time he did not mark the door.

Instead he counted the number of houses to the end of the street.

The next day the leader came back to Ali Baba's house with twenty donkeys.

Each donkey carried two large oil jars.

"My donkeys and I have traveled a long way,"
the leader said to Ali Baba. "May we spend
the night in your courtyard?"

"You may put the donkeys in the courtyard,"
said Ali Baba, "but you will be a guest
in my house."

The leader of the forty thieves thanked Ali
Baba and brought his donkeys into the courtyard.

He unloaded the oil jars and lined them up
against the wall.

When it was dark, the housekeeper tried to
light a lamp.

But her lamp was out of oil.

She went to the courtyard to get oil from
one of the jars.

"Is it time to come out?" whispered a voice
inside the jar.

Suddenly the housekeeper knew that there was
a thief hidden inside each of the forty jars.

In a deep voice she answered, "No, not yet."

Then she ran to tell Ali Baba what had happened.

Ali Baba hurried off
to get the sultan's soldiers.

The housekeeper showed
the leader to his room
and said good night.

The leader opened his
window and threw pebbles
at the oil jars as a
signal to the thieves.

Then he climbed down to the courtyard.
"Come out quietly," he said to the
forty thieves.

Suddenly the door burst open.
Ali Baba led the soldiers into
the courtyard.

The thieves fell down and broke the
oil jars in their hurry to get away.

But the leader and the forty thieves were all captured and led away to jail.

And the donkeys were taken to the sultan's stable.

The next day Ali Baba and his housekeeper worked hard to clean up the courtyard.

They told the sultan's soldiers about the
treasure in the cave and also about the gold
and jewels in their house.

Because they helped capture the thieves,
Ali Baba and his housekeeper were allowed to
keep part of the treasure.

They spent their gold carefully.

And they were never poor again.